DECK US ALL

Other Books by Walt Kelly

☆　☆　☆

with BOSTON CHARLIE

BY WALT KELLY

SIMON AND SCHUSTER • NEW YORK • 1963

TO ALL THE CHILDREN

In every color, shape
    and size,
And may they, singing,
    harmonize,
And may they sing
    in every weather,
And may they grow
    and grow together···

Again, the Newest Carol

Here's a version of one of the oldest
carols··· It constantly arrives, delightfully
surprising even those who have heard
it before···One old view of it is contained in
the sixth verse of the Wassail Song···

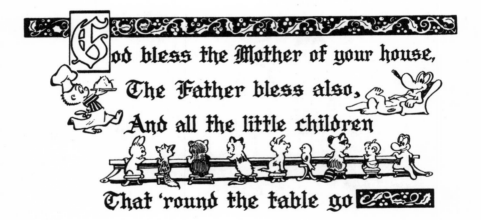

God bless the Mother of your house,
The Father bless also,
And all the little children
That 'round the table go

Meanwhile, the search goes on in this
book for the meaning and origins of
"Deck Us All...." Here we have several
"latest" words on the subject and no
last word at all ···

Contents

10

12

A LOOK AT THE POTLOOK THEORY ON THE ORIGIN OF D. U. A. W. B. C.

Herein the incredible conjecture of Professor Repent Potlook. It should be borne in mind that Jiggs Potlook vigorously belittled this theory, to the point that he retired to a life of counting sugar in Cleveland.

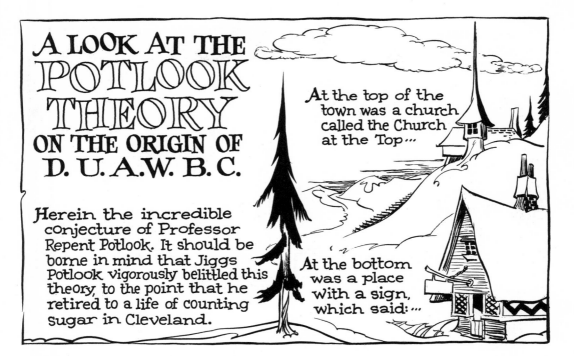

At the top of the town was a church called the Church at the Top...

At the bottom was a place with a sign, which said: ...

This is the HADES (NO TABLES FOR LADIES)

And every morning, thru drifts 19 feet deep, there would arrive a sorry apprentice carrying 450 lbs. of coal at exactly 5:00 p.m. on the dot.

16

20

When, what to his wond'ring
eyes should appear
But a miniature sleigh and
a tiny doll dear...

Hepzibah! That lovely name
Coursed thru his giddy brain
As dry leaves flee the
Hurricane!

Hastily disguising himself
as a choir boy, Nicodemus
hurried up the hill...

He threw open the
choir director's door and
declared himself!

My, what a surprise!

Inside, poor Nicodemus beheld his own apprentice
pulling taffy in tandem···

The Choir Director made
a startling suggestion:

Torn by a vibrant grief,
Nicodemus prudently made exit.

22

Back at the Hades, Nicodemus tried to drown his sorrow in Peppery Pot.

He thought of hanging···So he bought a length of rope on credit···(but decided to not sell tickets).

He decided tying it around his neck would be too painful··· Nic knotted the noose under his arms and lepped off.

As he fell on his··uh··floor and was turning around, Down the chimney St. Nicholas came with a bound.

23

St. Nicholas immediately pointed out the disadvantages of suicide⋯Nicodemus agreed.

Nic learned that his life-work (spoiling the carols) was a failure⋯

Then St. Nicholas offered Old Nic a job in the open. Nic accepted! Now when the two

Nora's freezin' on the trolley, Swaller dollar cauliflower, All-ey-ga-roo!

pass over Christmas Choir practice, children's voices waft the beloved carol into the wind.*

*Countless authorities contest this theory

CHRISTMAS CAN'T BE BEAT, NICK

I love trimming the tree
       with Trilby,
For Trilby has tresses true.
She *may* have an orb
On each side of her face
And it *may* be colored blue.

But her hair hangs down
      in blizzards,
All over her nose and teeth,
And her eyes,
      like little red lizards,
Peer out thru
      a Christmas wreath;

A wreath so greenly
      ridiculous
That I say,
    "This could be home,
Forget old St. Beatnikolas
And go buy your face a comb."

25

ANTI-MISTLE TOE TO TOE

I always thought
   a Parisite
Was a man who
    lived in France

But beneath
   the mistletoe
I learned who
   wears the pants.

So now I'm
   anti-mistle too,
For, in that
    kissing trance,

I first heard
   that twanging tune,
That tune
   to which I dance.

CHRISTMAS ON THE HARD-SELL

The Whimsical Wham
Of the huckstering
Ham

Who sells
  with a slam
The Christmas
  calam-

Ity known
  as the time
On the air
  that is prime

Convinces me I'm
**going
out of
my mime!**

BEDSIDE-CHIATRY

They're looking glum
into my head
And back, I'm looking, yes.
They cluck their tongues
And say, "My, my,"
The whole thing is a mess.
For what they see is
naught but nil
And what I see is less.

DIGITALIS

There's a nominal number
of numbers, you know,

But the more that they number, the number I grow.

My noggin is nimble
tho' normally numb,

My hat is a thimble,
my counter a thumb.

DIGITALIS

I fumble and figure
and fidget and fret,

And fearfully fly
from the digital wet.

My tax form is formless,
I quiver and quail,

I'll junk it, and jaded,
go joyful to jail.

32

"HE WAS ALSO KNOWED FAR AND WIDE AS A REMARKABLE SINGER... HIS VOICE WAS LIKE NO OTHER.

"ONE DAY OUR HANDSOME PRINCE BEHELD A BEAUTIFUL PRINCESS. HE IMMEDIATELY GOT A PAIN IN HIS STOMACH.

"HE DECIDED IT WAS LOVE AND NOT BREAKFAST AND OFFERED TO FIGHT ONE AND ALL FOR HER HAND...

"HOWEVER, BEING A MAN OF TRUE COMPASSION, THE PRINCE KNEW THAT SOMETHING MORE GENTEEL WAS NEEDED.

"THE FERTILE BRAIN OF THE PRINCE STRAIGHTWAY SPUN OUT A MASTERLY PLAN ···

"HE CALLED THE ROYAL POET AND HAD HIM DICTATE A SERENADE FOR THE LOVELY PRINCESS.

"HOWEVER, THO' THE PRINCE WAS A MAN OF MANY TALENTS, HE COULD WRITE BUT COULD NOT READ ··· SO, HE CALLED THE POET AGAIN ···

"HE LEARNED THE POET HAD READ WHAT HE'D WRITTEN, EATEN THE MANUSCRIPT AND JUMPED OUT OF THE WINDOW ···

SEASONING

Oh, I'll spend the winter resting
Just to find it interesting,
Or I may be hummer dinging
As I spend the summer singing.

In the springtime I'll be springing
And all Autumn I'll be winging
In the waning and the waxing
I'll be payning, they'll be taxing.

KNEADING THE NEEDLING NEED

There comes the wryly
moving cry
Upon a note resurgent,

"We have a matter, here,
my dear,
That's slightly more than
urgent."

We answer with a groan,
"My own,"
With something less
than sorrow,

"Nothing's so urgent now,
that won't
Be urgenter tomorrow."

INSIDE THE OUT

We fumble the thimble
And twinkle our toes
As all thru the year, dear,
We sniffle the snows.

We peanut our brittle
While weakly we weave
Roundly the hospital
To linger our leave.

Whether to, whither to?
Oh, wither not, friend,
Mind not the hitherto
And fear not the end.

THE LURK OF THE LIMURK

HERE'S ONE

The implacable, slackable
flack,
Sets sail on a backable
tack,
Close-hauled, his spinnaker
Gives him the ginnaker
To avoid and evade
an attack.

HERE'S ANOTHER

Oh, a placid Jack Acid
was said
To have sheets with no
eyeholes in bed,
"It's enough", giggled he,
"Taking snuff, I can see
All I want thru the hole
in my head."

F 13

The Thirteenth of Friday
 Is never yet my day.

Even if it came
 on Tues.
'Tis a day I would
 not choose.

Tho' I sometimes
 think it might
Be a sport and
 come at night.

The NORTHERNMOST POLL---

"H" is not for Herman,
Not for holly,
 not for heart,
"H" is just a letter
 Keeping "G" and "I"
 apart.

FACING EAST AT WEST AT ONCE

I really fear
There's nothing queer
In being as I am,
Because I've a head on either end
Does not mean there's much to mend,
I'm happy, happy, happy, happy,
Happy as a clam.

*I*f you find fault
With clams, my love,
Then, pray, find fault with me,
For **who** peers in that
      pearl-lined bed
And says,"Now, is that there
      its head
Or is that jelly just its belly,
What, oh, do I see?"

A LAMENT DIRECTED TO 212-555-1212

Oh, the wrangling ring of the Ringo McCoy
Is a jangling sting, oh, by jingo, **Ahoy**!
A fenangling thing is the lingo alloy
Of the numbers that never make bingo, my boy.

YOO HOO

Oh, hark, I have heard
    an angel sing,
Singing of all
    of the everything,

Singing for one
    and singing for all,
There must be one with
    an ear for the call.

Where, oh, where are you?
Where are you, you all?

Onward With High Hearts In Mouth

We're going to blank
some verse today
That has never been
blunk before.

And every time
we make a rhyme
It figures against
the score.

We'll think in terms
both big and black,
And blank and
blankety tragic.

With staring eyes
we'll ride the skies
In search of hophead
magic.

What we say will be
fair fraught
With a fright of utter
meaning---

And near the night
we'll dig the sight
Of the Pizza tourist
leaning.

We'll bring guitars,
disdain cigars,
And, sighing,
eschew shoes.

We'll hit a string
and numbly sing
Those big old
blank verse blues.

We rise, we rise to fall again,
Setting blazes in our hair ~~~

To make a light, for this, our night,
This swooning, sweet despair ~~~

The section that follows,
As night follows day,
Has some orphan swallows
And gaggles of gay,
Well-meaning jokesters
With japery fey,
Fritt'ring and flutt'ring
The Christmas away····

Bark Us All Bow~Wows of Folly
~One~

50

B U A B W O F
~ Two ~

54

Bark us all bow-wows of folly, Polly wolly cracker 'n' too-da-loo!
Hunky Dory's pop is lolly gaggin' on the wagon, Willy, folly go through!

Donkey bonny brays a carol, antelope cantaloup, 'lope with you!
Chollie's collie barks at Barrow, harum scarum five alarum bung-a-loo!

Xmas
Postludicrosity

58

T-Total
Recall

61

Peace on Earth, Goodwill to the Core

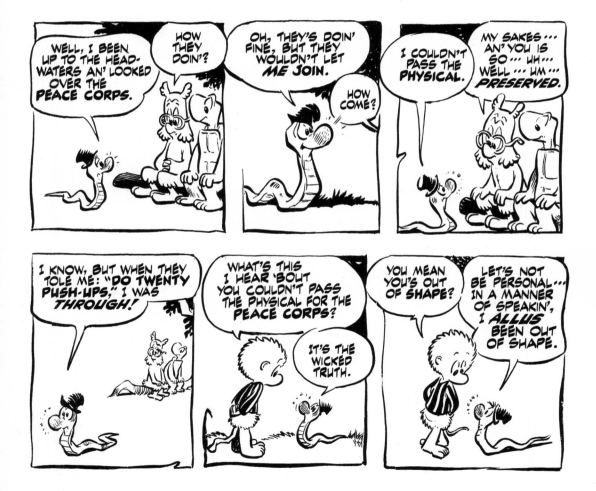

64

The
Hind Site
Is Where You Wind Up

70

The Five Major Senses
Add Up to a Nickel's Worth

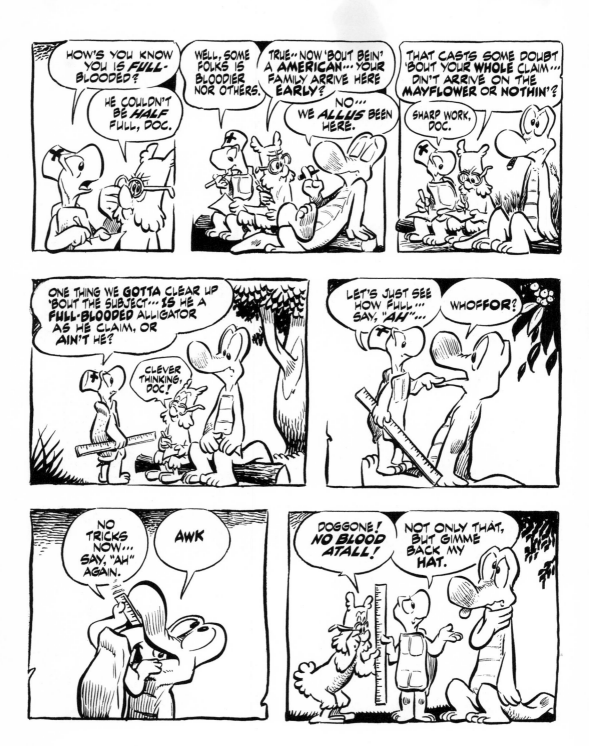

74

Some Laughs a Day Guaranteed to Keep the Doctor Away··· Far Away

A Bit about the
Off~Color Line

There's More to a Left Hook
Than Meats the Eye

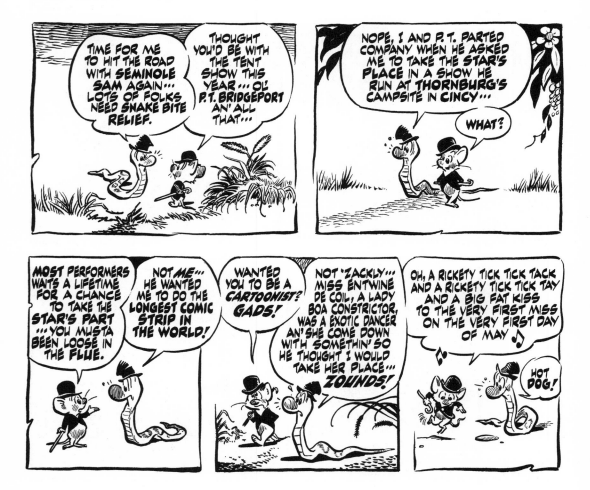

85

86

The Luck Is Sweetest
near the Bone

88

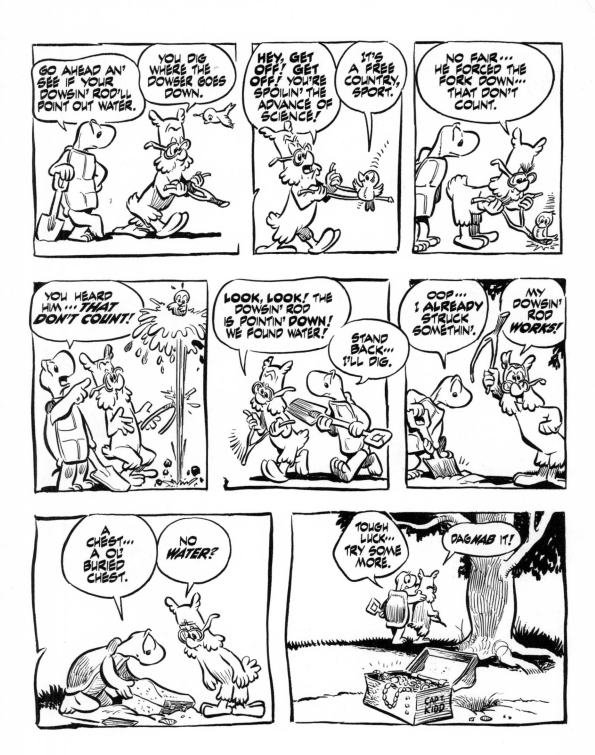

89

Music Makes the Fish Grow Flounder

Disremembering
the Unforgettable

94

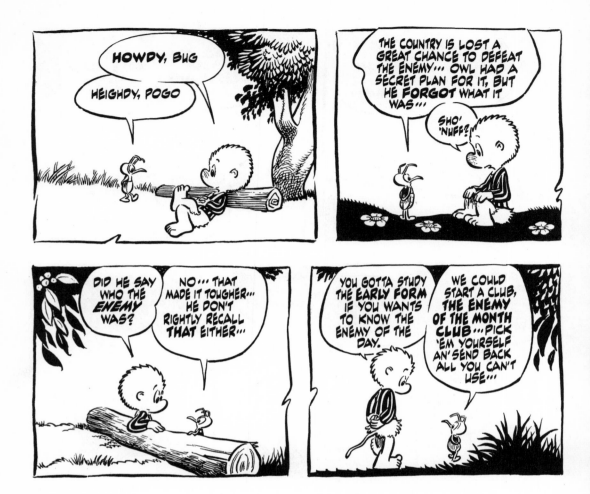

The Ides of February

To Arms! Us Women Are Revolting!

103

The Uncivil Rites of Women

106

108

The Mysterious Stranger···
Stranger Than Friction

111

A New Twist
on the Pretzel Queen

113

The Great Un-American Plan

116

117

Mirror, Mirror, on the Wall, Tell Me Who's the Squarest of Us All!

119

120

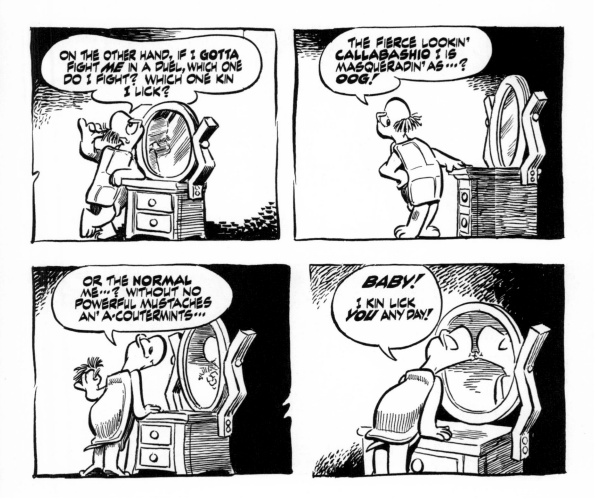

Here Benighthood
Is in Flower

123

BRIGHT CHRISTMAS LAND

WITH DECOROUS ABANDON

1 Here, O, here is a frolicking, Short, O, short little rollicking
2 Now, O, now jolly dancing men, Sing, O, sing as you're prancing, then

1 Shout, O, shout to the heavens our love, Love is at hand⋯
2 Know, O, know by the heavens our love Is for ev'ry man⋯

125

1 Watch, O, watch now a singing bird, High, high, high bonny winging bird
2 True love, love is a singing word, High, high wonderful winging word

1 Fly, O, fly through the stars to a bright Christmas Land...
2 Come all fly through the stars to our bright Christmas Land...

WITH APOLOGIES TO A YEAR GONE BY

The gentle journey
jars to stop,
The drifting dream
is done
And now we'll walk
As men have walked
Through years not
yet begun.
For Christmas is a
nightlong hope
And Hope the search
of years.
The gentle journey
wanders on
With laughter, love
and tears···